One White Sun

By Chiquita M. Hughes

Printed in the United States of America

Paperback ISBN: 978-1-7375427-1-1

Library of Congress Control Number:

Dedication:

To Isaiah, my first grandchild, the first great-grandchild for my parents—Lawrence and Betty Hughes, and the first great-great-grandchild held by my grandmother, Mrs. Irabelle Simmons White; this poem was inspired by our nature walks and your curiosity at the many creatures we would encounter and your observations along the way.

To my grandchildren, Isaiah, Cletis III, Elisha, Grace, and those to come. I thank God for you and I am blessed to have you and your parents.

One white sun
Shining high and bright
Red, orange, yellow, green
All colors in its light

Two green worms
Way way down
Creeping, crawling
All around

Three yellow finches
Nesting in a pine
Singing, tweeting
Merrily, sublime

Four white rabbits
Over in a field
Sleeping, peeking
Jumping, still

Five brown squirrels
In a maple tree
Hurrying, scurrying
So playfully

Six purple lilies
Swaying in the breeze
Bowing, waving
Elegantly

Seven olive-green turtles
Headed for the sea
Wobbling, sliding,
Clumsily

Eight red ladybugs
On an azalea bush
Gathering, swarming
Flitting, hushed

Nine light brown honeybees
On plants of rosemary
Collecting, feeding.
Helping, solitary

Ten orange clownfish
In a coral reef
Popping, clicking
Darting, free

Beauty, nature
Wonders I see
Colors, creatures
A symphony

Trees, flowers
Land, and sea
Sun, warmth
Life, energy

About the Author:

Chiquita Hughes has always loved poetry and children's books. She receives inspiration for writing through faith, family, and friends. Several years ago, she dreamed of writing children's books when her four children were small. As a grandmother, Chiquita is especially motivated to pursue this dream as she spends quality time with her four beautiful and precocious grand-children --Isaiah, Cletis III, Elisha, and Grace.

One White Sun

One White Sun explores the beauty of nature and begins with the sun, the source of life, warmth, and energy to Earth. This book is a counting poem and nature walk for children of all ages. Honeybees on plants of rosemary and olive-green turtles headed to sea are among other wonders to see. Enjoy the moments of living and non-living things through beautifully detailed illustrations. Be inspired to take a second look at nature and be in awe.
This book is a perfect tool for teaching science in early childhood and primary settings. Recommended ages: 3-8

Coming soon! One White Sun Curriculum Guides. Each guide will be available for purchase as an ebook or paperback. The guide provides STEM activities and links to resources for lessons at home and at school.

One White Sun
Curriculum Guide
By Chiquita M. Hughes

Also available for purchase on Amazon

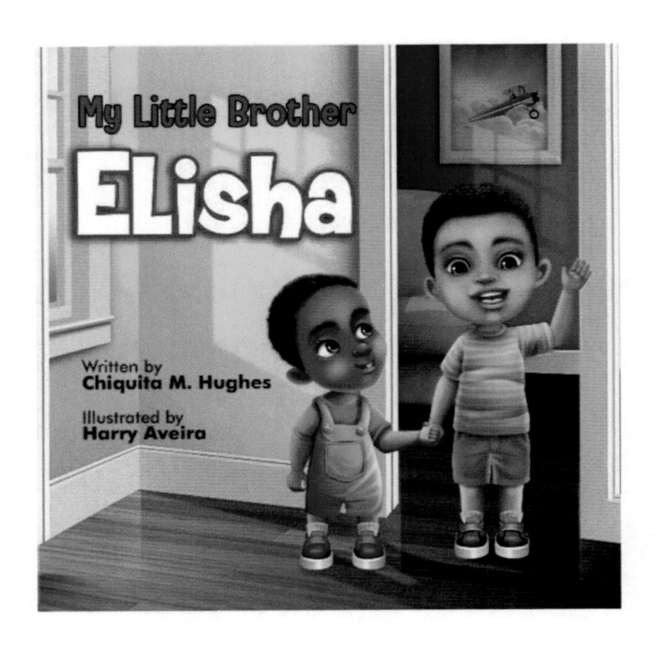

Made in the USA
Monee, IL
30 September 2023